THE ZOO AND THE CIRCUS

W 8762

written by Lucille Wood /designed and illustrated by Paul Taylor

bowmar

RHYTHMS TO READING
Book and Record Sets
A Multi-Sensory Approach to Music and Reading

A companion recording is available for this book and all others in the RHYTHMS TO READING series. Each picture in this book represents an action song or a descriptive musical composition which is included on the long-playing record.

The simple text under each picture provides a unique, multi-sensory experience for the young child. He reads about the activities to which he has just responded in movement and song. This text is also included on the recording for classroom use or at the listening post.

On the left-hand page, beginning on page 4, are printed the full story and song lyrics heard on the recording. This page is for the use of teachers, parents and children who have had reading experience.

Repetition is essential to learning. Learning which might otherwise be derived from tedious drill is here developed in an enjoyable, esthetic context.

Research indicates that children learn to read more quickly and easily words that are related to large muscle activity, esthetic experience and tongue-tickling rhymes.

When reading experiences are introduced through music, song and vigorous movement

- *memory is reinforced and tensions released, creating an atmosphere that encourages learning.*

- *the flow of language comes more naturally, encouraging the child to read in complete sentences.*

- *the number of clues which aid the child in reading are multiplied.*

- *word meanings are clarified and sight vocabulary is developed automatically.*

First Printing .... January 1971
Second Printing .... March 1972

We play in a circus band. Boom! Boom! Boom!

Let's have a circus today!
Everyone find an instrument to play
and we will have a circus band.
Look for drums, triangles,
finger cymbals, sandblocks, rhythm sticks
or other instruments that make a good sound,
and let's play a circus march.
After the band plays
it's time for the circus parade.
What do you want to be?

Who will be the circus horses
Circus horses stepping high?
Who will be the elephants,
Heavy elephants walking by?
Who will be the clumsy bear?
Who will be the tall giraffe?
Who will be the funny clowns?
Who will make the people laugh?
Who will play the big bass drum
And lead the parade, boom, boom?
Come on elephants and clowns,
Join the parade around the room.

4

We march in a circus parade. Left, right.

Now it is time for the circus show.
Who will be first? It's the bareback riders!
Let's be the horses
who gallop around the circus tent.
Here they come, a-gallop, a-gallop, a-gallop.

A-galloping, galloping, galloping by,
Circus horses, heads held high;
A-galloping, galloping, galloping go,
A-galloping, galloping, galloping, Whoa!
O lady, O lady, O lady tall,
Lovely lady, do not fall;
A-galloping, galloping, galloping go,
A-galloping, galloping, galloping, Whoa!

We gallop like circus horses.

How would it feel to be an elephant
with thick, big feet and legs
that are very heavy to lift off the ground?
As they walk, each elephant holds the tail
of the one in front with his trunk.
Sometimes an elephant does a dance,
standing on his back legs.
Let's all be elephants. Here they come.

We move like the big elephants.

We stand in a straight line
and get ready to walk the tightrope.
Balance with your arms. Be careful, do not fall.

We walk on the tightrope.

Make a big, round circle and we will play "balloon man."
Choose someone to be the man who sells balloons
to all the children. He will go in and out the circle.
When the music stops, he gives the balloons
to someone else who will be the new balloon man.

(1) Go in and out the circle,
  Go in and out the circle,
  Go in and out the circle,
  Who'll buy my red balloon?

(2) Go in and out the circle, etc.
  Who'll buy my green balloon?

(3) Go in and out the circle, etc.
  Who'll buy my blue balloon?

(4) Go in and out the circle, etc.
  Who'll buy my pink balloon?

(5) Go in and out the circle, etc.
  Who'll buy my white balloon?

We sell balloons at the circus.

We have a make-believe animal in our circus.
He is big and funny.

We have a make-believe animal in our circus.

Let's sit down and watch the clowns.
What do they tell us to do?

The first funny clown says, "Clap your hands."
The second funny clown says, "Wiggle your toes."
The third funny clown says, "Tap your feet."
The fourth funny clown says, "Wiggle your nose."
The fifth funny clown says, "Make a smile."
The sixth funny clown says, "Make a frown."
The seventh funny clown says, "Stand tall."
The eighth funny clown says, "Sit down."

The circus is over
and everyone marches out of the circus tent.

We do what the funny clowns do.

Do you know what day this is?

Today is the day we've been waiting for;
There's nothing to do that we like more
Than to go to the park and to go to the zoo
And visit our friend, Mister Kangaroo.

So come ev'ry one, it is time to go;
We walk along in a long, long row;
We will ride on the train and the merry-go-round,
A little red horse that goes up and down.

We skip through the gate of the zoo.

We are visiting the zoo.
We skip through the gate to see the animals.

Merrily we skip along, skip along, skip along,
Merrily we skip along, singing as we go.
(Repeat)

Listen! What animal is that?

Hello, hello, Mister Lion,
Living in the zoo;
Hello, hello, Mister Lion,
We can roar like you.

Like Mister Lion we walk around,
Walk, walk, walk;
Our big paws don't make a sound,
Walk, walk, walk.

We walk like a lion. Walk! Walk! Walk!

Let's go to the pool where the seals live.

Merrily we run along, run along, run along,
Merrily we run along, singing as we go.
(Repeat)

Listen!

Hello, hello, Mister Shiny Seal,
Living in the zoo;
Hello, hello, Mister Shiny Seal
We can bark like you.

We can clap our flippers:
Clap, clap, clap, clap, clap;
We can clap our flippers:
Flap, flap, flap, flap, flap, flap.

We clap our flippers like the seal. Clap! Clap! Clap!

It's time to rest awhile.
We sit on a bench and watch the monkeys
swinging from branch to branch in their big cages.
Let's count them.

One little, two little, three little monkeys,
Four little, five little, six little monkeys,
Seven little, eight little, nine little monkeys,
Living in the zoo.

Ten little, nine little, eight little monkeys,
Seven little, six little, five little monkeys,
Four little, three little, two little monkeys,
I'm a monkey too.

We watch the monkeys.

Let's go find the kangaroo.

Merrilly we walk along, walk along, walk along,
Merrily we walk along, singing as we go.
(Repeat)

Hello, hello, Mister Kangaroo,
Living in the zoo;
Hello, hello, Mister Kangaroo,
We can jump like you.

Jump, jump like a kangaroo,
Jump, jump, jump;
Jump, jump around the zoo,
Jump, jump, jump.

Where's the giraffe?

Merrily we jump along, jump along, jump along,
Merrily we jump along, singing as we go.

We jump like a kangaroo. Jump! Jump! Jump!

Look up there! It's the giraffe eating leaves
from the top of the tall tree.

Hello, hello, Mister Tall Giraffe,
Living in the zoo;
Hello, hello, Mister Tall Giraffe,
We can walk like you.

With long stiff legs we walk around,
Walk, walk, walk;
Our long, long necks move up and down,
Walk, walk, walk.

Merrily we walk along, walk along, walk along,
Merrily we walk along, singing as we go.
(Repeat)

We walk to the gate and out of the zoo
to take a ride on the merry-go-round.
Everyone gets on
and finds a horse that goes up and down.

Come take a ride, come take a ride
On the merry-go-round;
Come take a ride, come take a ride,
Round and round and around.

28

We move our long necks up and down like the giraffe.

Ding goes the bell, boom goes the drum,
On the merry-go-round;
Ding goes the bell, boom goes the drum,
Round and round and around.

Up and down, up and down,
On the merry-go-round;
Up and down, up and down,
Round and round and around.

Near the merry-go-round is a little black train.
Away we go around the track,
slowly, then faster and faster.

Our trip to the zoo is over,
so let's thank the animals.

Clap your hands for the merry-go-round,
The little red horse that goes up and down,
Clap your hands for the kangaroo,
And all the animals in the zoo.

Clap your hands for the seal and giraffe,
The funny monkeys that made us laugh,
Clap your hands for the ride on the little black train,
And for the day we come back again.

We ride the merry-go-round and a little black train.